ISBN: 0-9836089-0-3
ISBN 13: 978-0-9836089-0-5

You can visit us online at: **www.JacKrisPublishing.com**

Printed in the United States of America.

Ver. 1.0.0

Preface

We have designed this program to be a supplement to traditional grammar programs such as *Growing With Grammar*. It is therefore very helpful for the student to first understand the applicable underlying grammar concepts before attempting the coursework in this program.

This program is intended for all grades of students who understand grammar concepts at their appropriate grade levels. Therefore, students in early levels of grammar programs should not be expected to understand all of the coursework in this program.

This program consists of this workbook and an answer key.

At the beginning of the workbook is a table of contents that lists the concepts and the lessons that pertain to each.

Thank you for choosing **Digging Into Diagramming**. We look forward to the opportunity to provide you with the best tools possible to educate your children.

Table of Contents

Chapter 6 - Compound, Complex, and Compound-Complex Sentences

Chapter 7 - Diagramming Other Elements

Cross Reference to Growing With Grammar

SUBJECT	Grade Level					
	3	4	5	6	7	8
Chapter 1 - Subjects and Verbs						
Lesson 1 Sentences with One Subject and One Verb	X	X	X	X	X	X
Lesson 2 Sentences with the Subject Understood	X	X	X	X	X	X
Lesson 3 Sentences with a Compound Subject	X	X	X	X	X	X
Lesson 4 Sentences with a Compound Verb	X	X	X	X	X	X
Lesson 5 Sentences with a Compound Subject and a Compound Verb		X	X	X	X	X
Lesson 6 Verb Phrases (The lesson on helping verbs used with compound verbs is only taught in levels 6-8 of Growing With Grammar.)	X	X	X	X	X	X
Lesson 7 Questions	X	X	X	X	X	X
Lesson 8 Subject and Verb Review						
Chapter 2 - Adjectives and Adverbs						
Lesson 9 Adjectives	X	X	X	X	X	X
Lesson 10 Articles	X	X	X	X	X	X
Lesson 11 Predicate Adjectives				X	X	X	X
Lesson 12 Appositive Adjectives				X	X	X
Lesson 13 Adverbs that Modify Verbs	X	X	X	X	X	X
Lesson 14 Adverbs that Modify Adjectives				X	X	X
Lesson 15 Adverbs that Modify other Adverbs				X	X	X
Lesson 16 Adjective and Adverb Review						
Chapter 3 - Predicate Nouns, Direct Objects, and Indirect Objects						
Lesson 17 Predicate Nouns (The lessons on compound predicate nouns is taught in Growing With Grammar levels 5-8.)		X	X	X	X	X
Lesson 18 Direct Objects (The lessons on compound direct objects is taught in Growing With Grammar levels 5-8.)	X	X	X	X	X	X
Lesson 19 Direct Objects						X
Lesson 20 Direct Objects						X
Lesson 21 Indirect Objects				X	X	X	X
Lesson 22 Indirect Objects				X	X	X
Lesson 23 Predicate Noun, Direct Object, and Indirect Object Review						

SUBJECT	Grade Level					
	3	4	5	6	7	8
Chapter 4 - Prepositional Phrases						
Lesson 24 Adjective Prepositional Phrases		X	X	X	X	X
Lesson 25 Adverb Prepositional Phrases		X	X	X	X	X
Lesson 26 More about Prepositional Phrases				X	X	X
Lesson 27 Prepositional Phrase Review						
Chapter 5 - Verbals and Verbal Phrases						
Lesson 28 Participles and Participial Phrases						X
Lesson 29 Gerunds and Gerund Phrases						X
Lesson 30 Infinitives and Infinitive Phrases						X
Lesson 31 Verbal and Verbal Phrase Review						
Chapter 6 - Compound, Complex, and Compound-Complex Sentences						
Lesson 32 Compound Sentences				X	X	X
Lesson 33 Complex Sentences				X	X	X
Lesson 34 Complex Sentences				X	X	X
Lesson 35 Compound-Complex Sentences			New material			
Lesson 36 Compound, Complex, and Compound-Complex Sentence Review						
Chapter 7 - Diagramming Other Elements						
Lesson 37 Appositives			New material			
Lesson 38 Appositive Phrases					X	
Lesson 39 Interjections				X		X
Lesson 40 Nouns of Direct Address			New material			
Lesson 41 Diagramming Other Elements Review						

Chapter 1

Subjects and Verbs

Lesson 1   Sentences with One Subject and One Verb

Some **sentences** have **one subject** and **one verb**. The **subject** of the sentence is a noun or a pronoun and tells **who** or **what** the sentence is about. The **verb (predicate)** tells what the subject **does** or **is**.

The **subject** and **verb (predicate)** of a sentence are **diagrammed** on a horizontal line. The **subject** is placed on the left side of the diagram and the **verb** is placed on the right side. Use a short, vertical line to divide the subject area from the verb area.

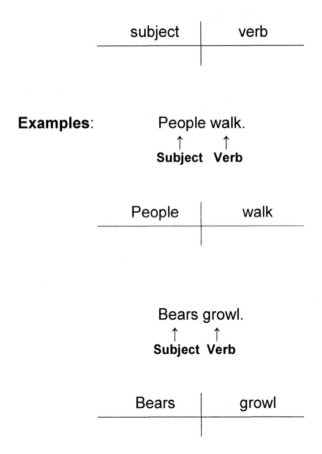

Examples:

When diagramming a sentence, remember to **capitalize** all words in the diagram as they are written in the sentence.

A. **Diagram** the **subject** and **verb** in these sentences.

1. Birds fly.

2. Telephones ring.

3. Fish swim.

4. Children laugh.

Lesson 2 <u>Sentences with the Subject Understood</u>

If the subject **you** is understood in a **command**, then write **you** in parentheses **(you)** in the **subject** area. The **verb** is placed in the **verb** area.

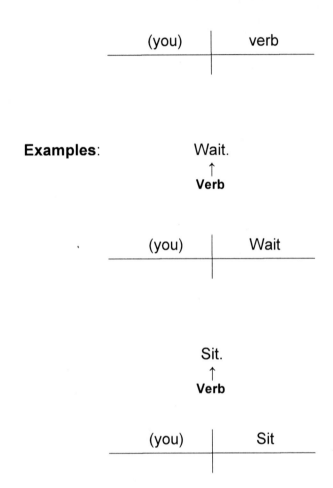

In these sentences, the **subject** is **not** stated. It is just understood that **you** is the **subject**, so **(you)** is placed in the subject area of the diagram.

3

A. **Diagram** the **subject** and **verb** in these sentences.

1. Help.

2. Whisper.

3. Eat.

4. Run.

Lesson 3   <u>Sentences with a Compound Subject</u>

Some **sentences** have a **compound subject** (**noun**). A **compound subject** is **two or more subjects** that share the same **verb**. A **conjunction** joins the **subjects**.

To **diagram** a sentence that contains **two subjects**, place the **subjects** on horizontal lines, one above the other, joined by diagonal lines. The **conjunction** in the sentence is written on a dotted line that connects the two subject lines. A short, vertical line divides the subject area from the **verb (predicate)** area, and the verb is placed on a line in the verb area.

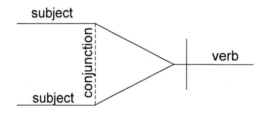

Examples: Howard and John play.

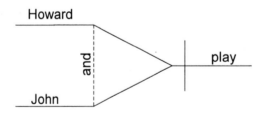

Eagles and hawks soar.

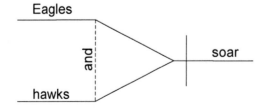

A. **Diagram** the **compound subject** and **verb** in these sentences.

1. Mom and Dad cooked.

2. Kyle and Landon won.

3. Dogs and cats run.

4. Henry and Shelly read.

Sentences with **more than two subjects** require one or more horizontal lines added to the subject area of the diagram. The **conjunction** in the sentence is then moved to the other side of the dotted line.

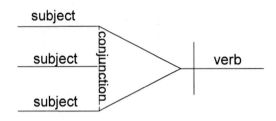

Examples: Sharks, whales, and dolphins swim.

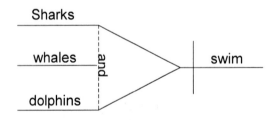

Helen, Robert, or Sarah sings.

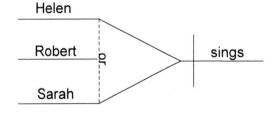

B. **Diagram** the **compound subject** and **verb** in these sentences.

1. Lions, tigers, and bears growl.

2. She, he, and I raced.

3. Dan, Joe, and Paul work.

4. Phil, Kay, and Becky waited.

Lesson 4   <u>Sentences with a Compound Verb</u>

Some **sentences** have a **compound verb**. A **compound verb** is **two or more verbs** that tell what the subject is doing. A **conjunction** joins the **verbs**.

To **diagram** a sentence that contains two **verbs**, place the **subject** on a horizontal line. A short, vertical line divides the **subject** area from the **verb** area. The **verbs** are placed on two horizontal lines, one above the other, joined by diagonal lines. The **conjunction** in the sentence is written on a dotted line that connects the two **verb** lines.

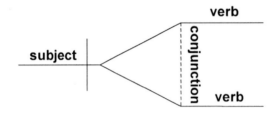

Examples: Boys ran and played.
          ↑   ↑   ↑
      Subject Verb   Verb

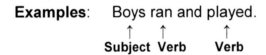

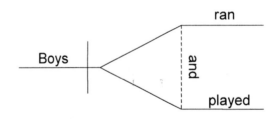

Dogs walk or run.
   ↑   ↑   ↑
Subject Verb   Verb

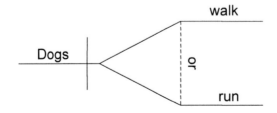

A. **Diagram** the **subject** and **compound verb** in these sentences.

1. Ducks quack or waddle.

2. Cars slowed and stopped.

3. Tyler swung and missed.

4. People came and left.

Sentences with **more than two verbs** require one or more horizontal lines added to the verb area of the diagram. The **conjunction** in the sentence is then moved to the other side of the dotted line.

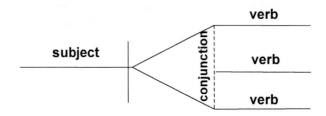

Examples: Caroline writes, draws, and paints.

    ↑   ↑   ↑   ↑
   Subject **Verb** **Verb** **Verb**

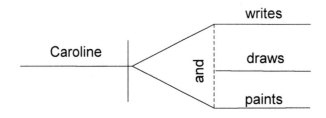

Babies cry, sleep, or eat.

   ↑ ↑ ↑   ↑
  Subject **Verb** **Verb** **Verb**

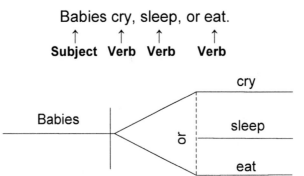

       11

B. **Diagram** the **subject** and **compound verb** in these sentences.

1. Mark swims, runs, and bikes.

2. He came, saw, and conquered.

3. Mom dusts, cleans, or vacuums.

4. Kyle ran, jumped, and won.

Lesson 5 <u>Sentences with a Compound Subject and a Compound Verb</u>

Sentences often have both a **compound subject** and a **compound verb**.

To diagram a sentence that contains a **compound subject** and a **compound verb**, place the **subjects** on the left side on horizontal lines, one above the other, joined by diagonal lines. The **conjunction** is written on a dotted line that connects the **subject** lines. A short, vertical line divides the **subject** area from the **verb** area. The **verbs** are placed on horizontal lines, one above the other, joined by diagonal lines. The **conjunction** is written on a dotted line that connects the **verb** lines.

Sentences with **two subjects** and **two verbs** are diagrammed like this:

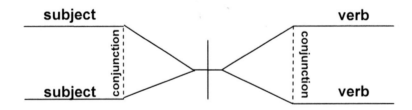

Example:

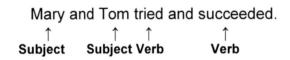

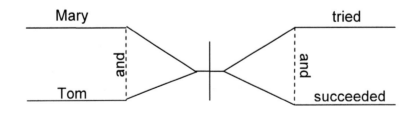

A. **Diagram** the **compound subject** and **compound verb** in these sentences.

1. Girls and boys read and write.

2. Mom and Dad cooked and cleaned.

3. Cheryl and Tom clap and cheer.

4. Children and parents laugh and talk.

Sentences with **more than two subjects** and **two verbs** are diagrammed like this:

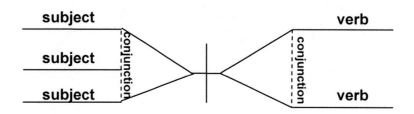

Remember to move the **conjunction** to the other side of the dotted line connecting the **subjects** when there are more than two subjects.

Example: Henry, Kayla, and Harper worked and played.

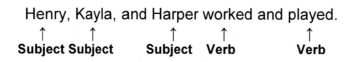

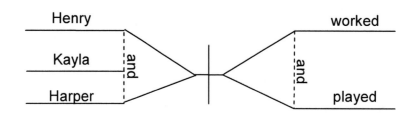

B. **Diagram** the **compound subject** and **compound verb** in these sentences.

1. Lions, tigers, and cougars hunt and eat.

2. Ron, Sue, and Lynn competed but lost.

3. Bees, wasps, and hornets buzz and sting.

4. Todd, Marie, and I watched and waited.

Sentences with **two subjects** and **more than two verbs** are diagrammed like this:

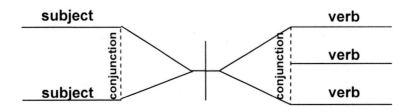

Remember to move the **conjunction** to the other side of the dotted line connecting the **verbs** when there are more than two verbs.

Example: Hawks and eagles soar, hunt, and perch.

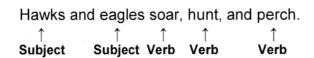

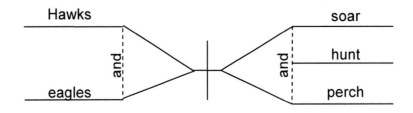

C. **Diagram** the **compound subject** and **compound verb** in these sentences.

1. Mothers or fathers teach, care, and nurture.

2. Dogs or puppies dig, run, and play.

3. Marla and Tom sat, looked, and listened.

4. Groundhogs and chipmunks dig, eat, and sleep.

Sentences with **more than two subjects** and **more than two verbs** are diagrammed like this:

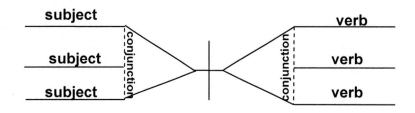

Remember to move the **conjunction** to the other side of the dotted line connecting the **subjects** and the **verbs**.

Example: Max, Robert, and John jumped, tripped, and slid.

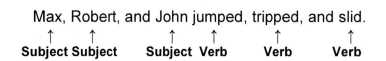

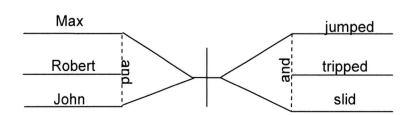

D. **Diagram** the **compound subject** and **compound verb** in these sentences.

1. Men, women, and children clapped, cheered, and whistled.

2. Kristin, Jacob, and Joshua swam, splashed, and dove.

3. Lions, tigers, and leopards prowl, hunt, and eat.

4. Kelly, Rebecca, and Stella laughed, ran, and played.

Lesson 6   <u>Verb Phrases</u>

Some sentences contain a **verb phrase**. A **verb phrase** contains a **main verb** and all of its **helping verbs**.

On a sentence **diagram**, the **helping verbs** are placed before the **main verb** in the **verb** area of the **diagram**.

subject	verb phrase

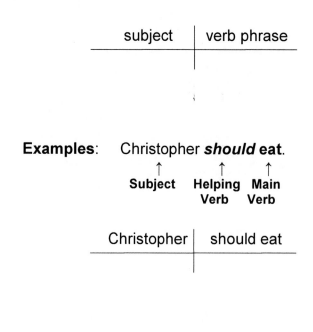

Examples: Christopher *should* eat.

Christopher	should eat

You *could have been* exercising.

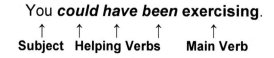

You	could have been exercising

     21

A. **Diagram** the **subject** and **verb phrase** in these sentences.

   1. You must leave.

   2. She will be singing.

   3. Shane might have been sleeping.

   4. Dad will be raking.

Sometimes a **helping verb** is used with a **compound verb**. If both **verbs** of the compound verb **share** the **helping verb**, then place the **helping verb** on the line after the vertical line that follows the subject area.

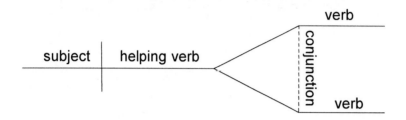

The way to determine if the **helping verb** is shared by both verbs is to try the helping verb with both verbs in the sentence to see if the sentence still makes sense.

Brian **did run** and **fall**.

↓

Brian **did run** and **did fall**.

In this example, the **helping verb** makes sense with both verbs.

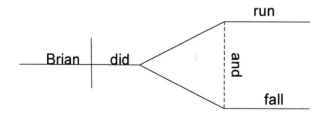

23

B. **Diagram** the **subject** and **verb phrase** in these sentences.

1. He must stop and rest.

2. Night has come and gone.

3. Mike will talk or listen.

4. Audiences had clapped and cheered.

If only one of the **verbs** uses the **helping verb**, then place the **helping verb** on the **verb** line with its corresponding **verb**.

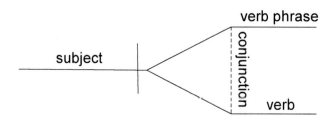

Again, if you try the **helping verb** with both verbs in the sentence, you will see if the sentence makes sense.

Sherry <u>**was**</u> **leaning** and **fell**.

↓

Sherry <u>**was**</u> **leaning** and <u>**was**</u> **fell**.

In this example, the helping verb only makes sense with the first verb **leaning**. On the sentence diagram, the helping verb **was** will be placed on the verb line with the verb **leaning**.

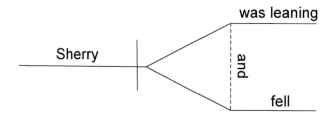

C. **Diagram** the **subject**, **verb**, and **verb phrase** in these sentences.

1. Dad was painting but finished.

2. Mia was laughing and smiled.

3. Computers were flashing but stopped.

4. He was walking and tripped.

Lesson 7   Questions

To diagram a **question**, you must rephrase the **question** as a **statement**. This will place the **subject** before the **verb**.

Did Amanda win?

↓

Amanda **did win**.

You can now diagram this **question** just as you would any sentence that has a subject and a verb phrase.

Amanda	Did win

Was she eating?

↓

She **was eating**.

she	Was eating

Capitalize words in the **diagram** as they were written in the original **question**.

A. **Diagram** the **subject** and **verb phrase** in these questions.

1. Can you wait?

2. Should we have been listening?

3. Is she eating?

4. Could you have waited?

Lesson 8   <u>**Subject and Verb Review**</u>

A. **Diagram** the **subject** and **verb** in these sentences.

   1. Shelly hurried.   2. Stop.

B. **Diagram** the **compound subject** and **verb** in these sentences.

   1. Flowers and trees grow.   2. Rita, Clark, and Fiona hid.

C. **Diagram** the **subject** and **compound verb** in these sentences.

   1. Cars stop and park.

   2. Balloons rose, floated, and popped.

D. **Diagram** the **compound subject** and **compound verb** in these sentences.

1. Firefighters and officers serve and protect.

2. Chipmunks and squirrels ran, jumped, and played.

3. Actors, dancers, and singers practice and perform.

4. Bart, Matt, and Robert talked, wrote, and studied.

E. **Diagram** the **subject** and **verb phrase** in these sentences.

1. Harold should have been exercising.

2. I have learned and succeeded.

3. Dan was coughing and choked.

4. Should you be sleeping?

Chapter 2

Adjectives and Adverbs

Lesson 9   <u>Adjectives</u>

An **adjective** modifies or describes a **noun** in a sentence. On a sentence **diagram**, place each **adjective** on a slanted line beneath the noun it describes. If there is more than one adjective, each adjective is written on a separate diagonal line.

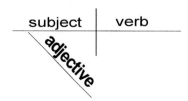

Examples: **Huge** *waves* crashed.
                    ↑   ↑   ↑
          Adjective Subject   Verb

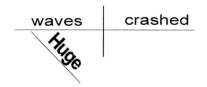

Two fast *boys* and **three competitive** *girls* raced.
  ↑   ↑   ↑   ↑   ↑   ↑   ↑
Adjectives Subject   Adjectives   Subject Verb

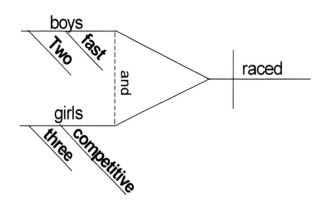

A. **Diagram** the **subject**, **verb**, and each **adjective** in these sentences.

1. Many beautiful butterflies flew.

2. Three small colorful kites soared.

3. Those happy girls and that cheerful boy played.

4. Four large black trucks and one small white car passed.

Lesson 10   <u>Articles</u>

The **articles a**, **an**, and **the** are diagrammed in the same manner as an **adjective**. Place an **article** below the **noun** to which it refers.

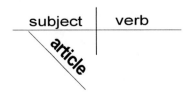

Examples: **The** tired infant cried.

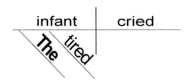

An eagle and **a** brown hawk soared.

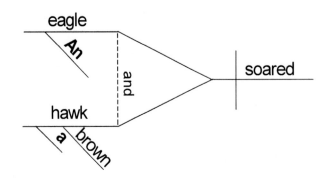

35

A. **Diagram** the **subject**, **verb**, and each **adjective** and **article** in these sentences.

1. A beautiful blue butterfly flew.

2. The angry dog barked.

3. A meteor and an asteroid fell.

4. A large rose and a small daisy bloomed.

Lesson 11   <u>Predicate Adjectives</u>

A **predicate adjective** is an **adjective** that follows a **linking verb** to describe the subject of the sentence. On a sentence diagram, place the **predicate adjective** on the same line with the **subject** and **linking verb**. The **predicate adjective** is separated from the **linking verb** by a short diagonal line that does not break through the horizontal line.

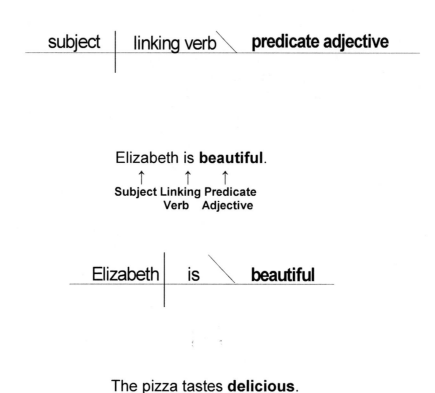

Examples:

Elizabeth is **beautiful**.

The pizza tastes **delicious**.

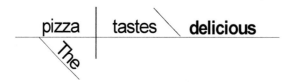

A. **Diagram** the **subject**, **linking verb**, and **predicate adjective** in these sentences. Make sure to diagram any **articles** and **adjectives** in each sentence as well.

1. That tall dancer is graceful.

2. My younger sister seems sad.

3. Those boys are talented.

4. The yellow cheese smells fresh.

On a sentence **diagram**, place each **adjective** of a **compound predicate adjective** after the diagonal line on horizontal lines, one above the other, joined by diagonal lines. Place the **conjunction** on a dotted line that connects the **predicate adjective** lines.

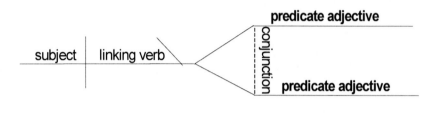

Examples: That lasagna *tastes* **hot** and **delicious**.

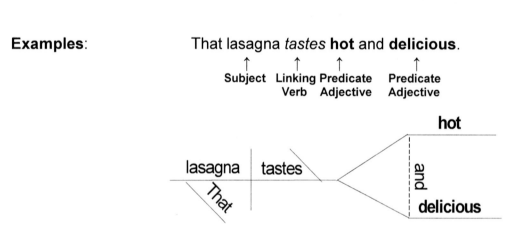

Remember, if the sentence has **more than two predicate adjectives**, the **conjunction** is moved to the other side of the dotted line.

The basketball *is* **deflated**, **damaged**, and **useless**.

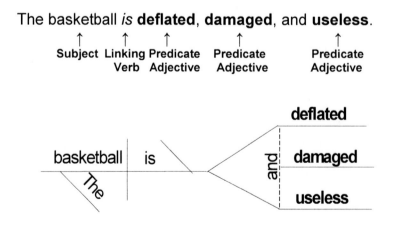

B. **Diagram** the **subject**, **linking verb**, and each **predicate adjective** in these sentences. Make sure to diagram any **articles** and **adjectives** in each sentence as well.

1. The new car was black and red.

2. This old, brown blanket feels hot and scratchy.

3. My father was hungry, thirsty, and tired.

4. The milk smelled old, sour, and disgusting.

Lesson 12   Appositive Adjectives

An **appositive adjective** modifies the **noun** or **pronoun** it follows. **Appositive adjectives** usually come in **pairs** and are **joined** by a **conjunction**. On a sentence **diagram**, **appositive adjectives** are diagrammed under the word they modify. A dotted line connects the two **appositive adjectives** and the **conjunction** is placed on it.

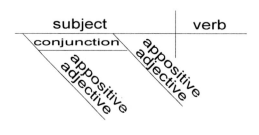

Examples: Peter, **tired** and **hungry**, was irritable.

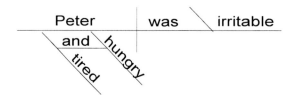

The motorcycle, **fast** and **shiny**, was new.

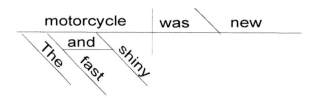

A. **Diagram** these sentences with **appositive adjectives**.

1. The strawberries, red and ripe, taste sweet.

2. That large fire, yellow and warm, crackled.

3. The small boy, bored and exhausted, cried.

4. Mom's bread, fresh and warm, smells delicious.

Lesson 13   <u>Adverbs that Modify Verbs</u>

Adverbs are words that tell us more about other words such as **verbs**, **adjectives**, or other **adverbs** by telling **how**, **when**, **where**, **how often**, or **to what extent**.

<u>Adverbs that Modify Verbs</u>

On a sentence **diagram**, an **adverb** is placed on a slanted line under the **verb** it describes.

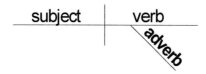

Examples: Jacob leaves **soon**.
                        ↑   ↑   ↑
                  Subject   Verb   Adverb

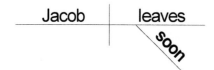

Carefully the girl listened.
        ↑   ↑   ↑
   Adverb   Subject   Verb

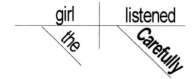

A. **Diagram** these sentences with **adverbs that describe verbs**.

1. The ants slowly marched.

2. Yesterday the snow fell.

3. My friend skates gracefully.

4. The noisy children played outside.

Lesson 14   <u>Adverbs that Modify Adjectives</u>

Adverbs don't just modify **verbs**. They can also modify **adjectives**.

<u>Adverbs that Modify Adjectives</u>

On a sentence **diagram**, an **adverb** is placed on a slanted line under the **adjective** or **predicate adjective** it describes.

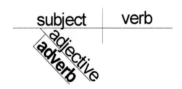

Examples: The **very** excited crowd cheered.

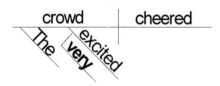

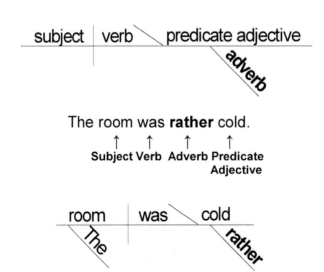

A. **Diagram** these sentences with **adverbs that describe adjectives**.

1. The very patient boy sat quietly.

2. That spicy food was extremely delicious.

3. Ben is an extremely smart boy.

4. Many very young people swim.

Lesson 15   Adverbs that Modify Other Adverbs

Adverbs can also tell us more about **other adverbs**.

Adverbs that Modify Other Adverbs

On a sentence **diagram**, an **adverb** is placed on a slanted line under the **adverb** it describes.

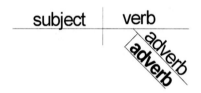

Examples: Joanne **very** quietly whispered.
                    ↑   ↑   ↑   ↑
                Subject Adverb Adverb   Verb

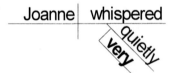

The three girls swam **quite** lazily.
        ↑   ↑   ↑   ↑
    Subject   Verb   Adverb Adverb

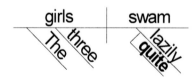

47

A. **Diagram** these sentences with **adverbs that describe other adverbs**.

1. My father snored very noisily.

2. The truck quite loudly grumbled.

3. My sister studied extremely carefully.

4. Shelly talks incredibly softly.

Lesson 16   <u>Adjective and Adverb Review</u>

A. **Diagram** the **subject**, **verb**, and each **adjective** in these sentences.

   1. One large blue kite soared.

   2. Hot wheat bread smelled tasty.

B. **Diagram** the **subject**, **verb**, and each **article** in these sentences.

   1. The lioness watched and waited.

   2. A camel and an elephant strolled.

C. **Diagram** these sentences with **predicate adjectives**.

1. That movie was scary but fun.

2. Mom's soup tastes delicious.

D. **Diagram** these sentences with **appositive adjectives**.

1. Talia, tall and skinny, is graceful.

2. The test, long and dull, was hard.

E. **Diagram** these sentences with **adverbs that describe verbs**.

  1. Earlier my father mowed.

  2. The two girls ran outside.

F. **Diagram** these sentences with **adverbs that describe adjectives**.

  1. The very talented chef cooked.

  2. Kristin seems extremely happy.

G. **Diagram** these sentences with **adverbs that describe other adverbs**.

1. The child cries surprisingly loudly.

2. Very quickly Marla ate.

Chapter 3

Predicate Nouns, Direct Objects, and Indirect Objects

Lesson 17   <u>**Predicate Nouns**</u>

A **predicate noun** is a **noun** that follows a **linking verb** to **rename** or **identify** the **subject** of the sentence. On a sentence diagram, place the **predicate noun** on the same line with the **subject** and **linking verb**. The **predicate noun** is separated from the **linking verb** by a short **diagonal line** that does not break through the horizontal line. Notice that a **diagonal** (or a **slanted line**) is always used to separate a **linking verb** from whatever follows it on the sentence diagram.

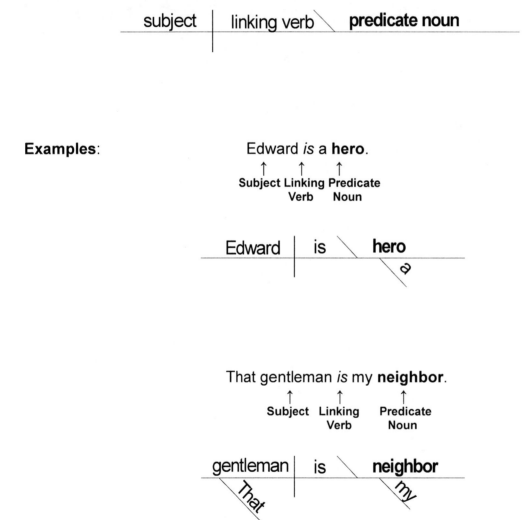

Examples:

Edward *is* a **hero**.

Subject Linking Predicate
         Verb   Noun

That gentleman *is* my **neighbor**.

Subject Linking Predicate
         Verb   Noun

B. **Diagram** these sentences with **compound predicate nouns**.

1. He became a husband and a father.

2. These flowers are roses and peonies.

3. My good friends are Rebecca and Amy.

4. My pets are a black dog and a white cat.

Lesson 18   **Direct Objects**

A **direct object** is the **noun** or **pronoun** that follows an **action verb** and receives the **action** from that **verb**. It answers **whom** or **what** after the **verb**. On a sentence **diagram**, place the **direct object** on the same line as the **subject** and the **action verb**. Separate the **direct object** from the **action verb** with a short vertical line that does not break through the horizontal line. Notice that a **vertical line** is always used to separate an **action verb** from whatever follows it on the sentence diagram.

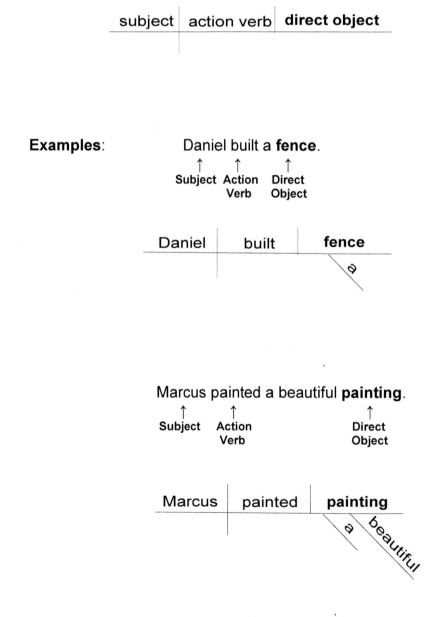

Examples: Daniel built a **fence**.

A. **Diagram** these sentences with **direct objects**.

1. My mother wrote a long letter.

2. The happy tourists visited France.

3. Dad quickly read the newspaper.

4. The candidate gave a great speech.

To diagram a **compound direct object**, place each **direct object** after the short vertical line that separates the action verb on a horizontal line, one above the other, joined by diagonal lines. Write the **conjunction** on the dotted line that connects the **direct object** lines.

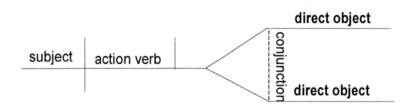

Examples: The carpenter built a **house** and a **garage**.

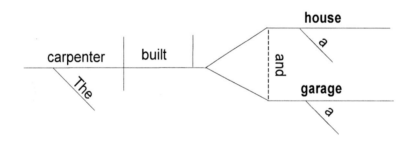

Grandma baked delicious **cakes** and scrumptious **cookies**.

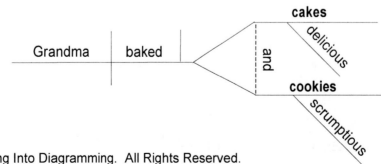

B. **Diagram** these sentences with **compound direct objects**.

1. Yesterday I saw Melissa and Mark.

2. Marty bought a red kite and a blue bike.

3. Dad reads magazines and newspapers daily.

4. Tomorrow I will buy a hat and mittens.

Move the **conjunction** to the **other side** of the dotted line when there are **more than two direct objects**.

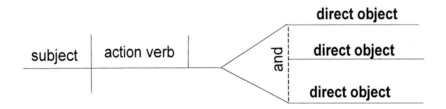

Examples: Charlie *plays* **basketball**, **football**, and **soccer**.

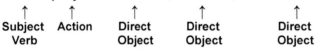

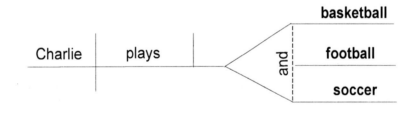

Angelina *mailed* a **postcard**, two **letters**, and a **package**.

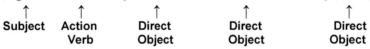

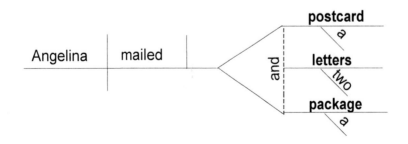

C. **Diagram** these sentences with **compound direct objects**.

1. My mother cooked peas, carrots, and corn.

2. Melissa collects white shells, old stamps, and shiny rocks.

3. The worker painted the new house, the large garage, and the old fence.

4. The electrician repairs outlets, sockets, and wiring.

Lesson 19   <u>Direct Objects</u>

Sometimes each **verb** of a **compound verb** has its own **direct object**. When this occurs, **diagram** each **direct object** after its corresponding **verb**. Write the **conjunction** on the dotted line that connects the **verb/direct object** line.

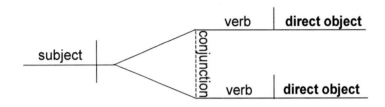

Examples: Brandon *caught* the new **ball** and *dropped* his favorite **mitt**.

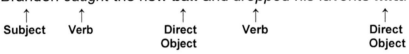

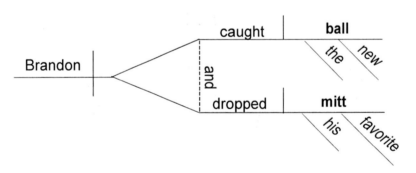

Angelo *baked* fresh **bread** and *cooked* delicious **pasta**.

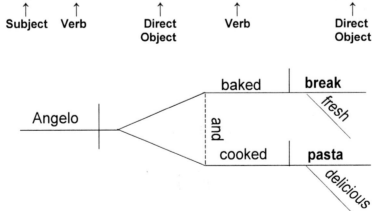

A. **Diagram** these sentences with **direct objects**.

1. My sister vacuumed the dirty rug and dusted the glass table.

2. The three happy girls played a game and sang a silly song.

3. Mom opened the large windows and closed the door.

4. Charlie drew a beautiful picture and read a long story.

Lesson 20   <u>Direct Objects</u>

Sometimes the **verbs** of a **compound verb** share a **direct object**. When this occurs, place the **direct object** on a horizontal line after a short vertical line joined by diagonal lines that are connected to the verb lines. Write the **conjunction** on the dotted line that connects the **verb** line.

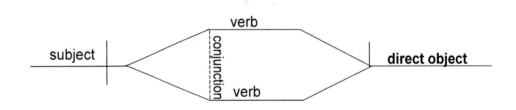

Examples: My sister *brushed* and *flossed* her **teeth**.

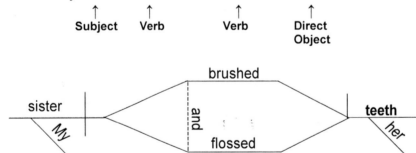

We *bought* and *planted* many small **seeds**.

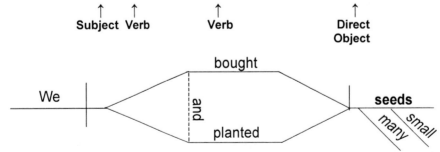

A. **Diagram** these sentences with **direct objects**.

1. Our family cooked and ate delicious lasagna.

2. My extremely talented friend wrote and sang that beautiful song.

3. That very gifted architect designed and built our amazing house.

4. Marla wrapped and sent a surprise present.

Lesson 21   <u>Indirect Objects</u>

An **indirect object** is a **noun** or **pronoun** that precedes a **direct object** and tells **to whom** or **to what**, or **for whom** or **for what** the **action** of the **verb** is done. On a sentence diagram, place the **indirect object** below the **verb** on a horizontal line connected to the **verb** by a diagonal line.

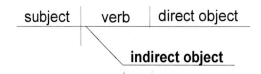

Examples: Karla handed her **aunt** the *keys*.

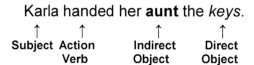

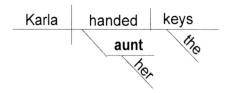

My father gave **me** some cold *water*.

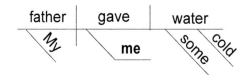

A. **Diagram** these sentences with **indirect objects**.

1. Chris gave Katie hockey tickets.

2. The waiter served us our food.

3. Daniel wrote his father a long letter.

4. Ed sold Steve his old bicycle.

Lesson 22   Indirect Objects

Sentences often have **more than one indirect object**. This is called a **compound indirect object**. On a sentence **diagram**, place the **indirect objects** of a **compound indirect object** below the **verb** on two horizontal lines, one above the other, joined by diagonal lines. This is connected to the **verb** by a diagonal line. Write the **conjunction** on a dotted line that connects the two **indirect object** lines.

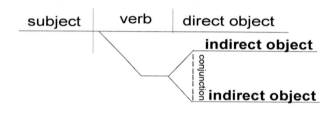

Examples: Daniel left **Tommy** and **me** a *message*.

 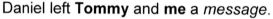

| Subject | Action Verb | Indirect Object | Indirect Object | Direct Object |

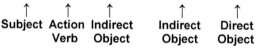

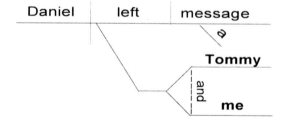

Ariel showed **Jake** and **Brooke** her new red *bicycle*.

| Subject | Action Verb | Indirect Object | Indirect Object | Direct Object |

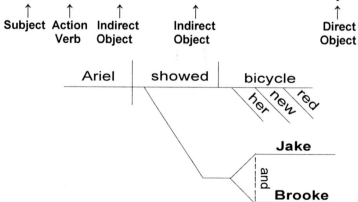

71

A. **Diagram** these sentences with **compound indirect objects**.

1. Bradley told his brother and my sister the funny joke.

2. This book gave Alexa and Sally the important information.

3. Margaret asked her mother and her father a question.

4. My sister fed the dog and the cat some treats.

Lesson 23   Predicate Noun, Direct Object, and Indirect Object Review

A. **Diagram** these sentences with **predicate nouns**.

   1. My neighbor was a teacher.

   2. Sarah is a skilled musician.

B. **Diagram** these sentences with **compound predicate nouns**.

   1. Your lotion smells sweet and fragrant.

   2. The tie is cotton or polyester.

C. **Diagram** these sentences with **direct objects**.

1. Pamela bought a new dress.

2. I carried Dan's heavy backpack.

D. **Diagram** these sentences with **compound direct objects**.

1. My father reads magazines and books.

2. Natalie drew a bird, a house, and a tree.

E. **Diagram** these sentences with **direct objects**.

1. Charlie planted blue flowers and trimmed the bushes.

2. I drank a chocolate milkshake and ate a delicious hamburger.

F. **Diagram** these sentences with **direct objects**.

1. My mother bought and wore a beautiful sweater.

2. Sarah washed and dried the dishes.

G. **Diagram** these sentences with **indirect objects**.

1. I gave the dog a bath.

2. My bother told me his plans.

H. **Diagram** these sentences with **compound indirect objects**.

1. Mary made John and Kay some popcorn.

2. The cashier handed Madeline and me the money.

Chapter 4

Prepositional Phrases

Lesson 24   Adjective Prepositional Phrases

A **prepositional phrase** can act like an **adjective** by modifying a **noun**. It comes immediately after the word it modifies and tells **what kind**, **how many**, or **which one**.

On a sentence diagram, an **adjective prepositional phrase** is placed below the **noun** it describes, similar to an **adjective**.

Place the **preposition** on a diagonal line beneath the word it modifies. The **object of the preposition** is placed on a horizontal line attached to it. Modifiers of the **object of the preposition** are placed on diagonal lines beneath the object.

Modifying a Subject

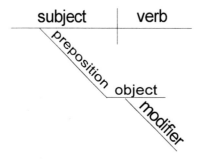

Example Modifying a Subject:

The *dog* **with black spots** ran fast.

Subject   Adjective Prepositional Phrase

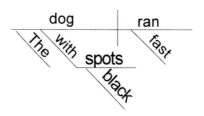

Modifying a Direct Object

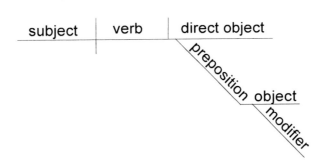

Example Modifying a Direct Object:

We made *pizza* **with spicy pepperoni**.

↑ Direct Object ↑ Adjective ↑ Prepositional Phrase

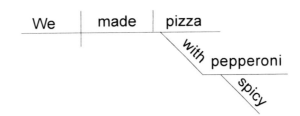

~~~~~~

Modifying an Indirect Object

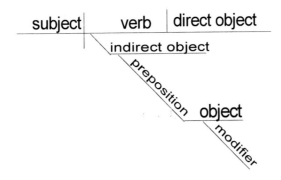

Example Modifying an Indirect Object:

I gave my *friend* **across the street** a gift.

↑ Indirect Object ↑ Adjective ↑ Prepositional Phrase

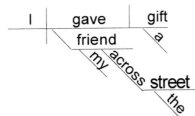

Modifying a Predicate Noun

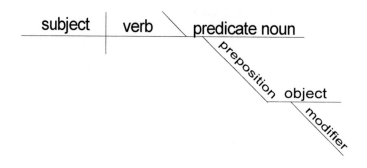

**Example Modifying
a Predicate Noun:**

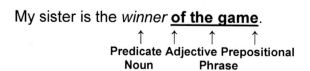

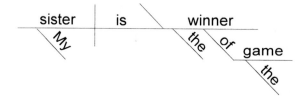

A. **Diagram** these sentences with **adjective prepositional phrases**.

1. The baby in the crib is cute.

2. I received a brochure about Europe.

3. The waiter brought the customer in the booth a cracker.

4. James is the boy near the fence.

Lesson 25   <u>**Adverb Prepositional Phrases**</u>

A **prepositional phrase** can also act like an **adverb** by modifying a **verb**, **adjective**, or **adverb**. This is called an **adverb prepositional phrase** and can appear **anywhere** in the sentence. It tells **how**, **when**, **where**, **how often**, or **to what extent**.

Place the **preposition** on a diagonal line beneath the word it modifies. The **object of the preposition** is placed on a horizontal line attached to it. Modifiers of the **object of the preposition** are placed on diagonal lines beneath the object.

<u>**Modifying a Verb**</u>

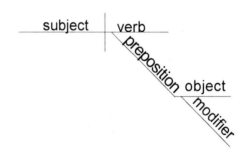

Example Modifying
a Verb: The girls *ran* **<u>around the track</u>**.
                              ↑   ↑   ↑   ↑
                          Verb Adverb Prepositional
                                   Phrase

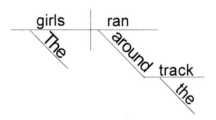

83

Modifying an Adjective

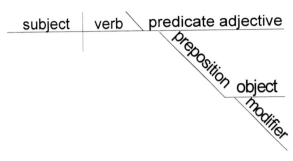

**Example Modifying a
Predicate Adjective**:

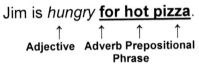

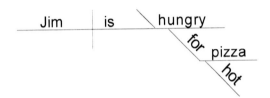

**Example Modifying
an Adjective:**

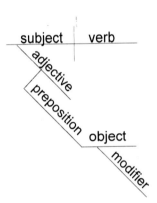

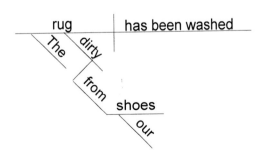

84

Modifying an Adverb

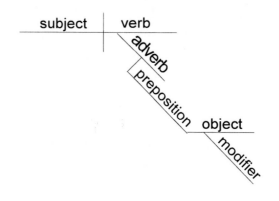

**Example Modifying
an Adverb:**

The travelers arrived *late* **during the night**.

Adverb   Adverb Prepositional
Phrase

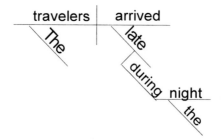

85

A. **Diagram** these sentences with **adverb prepositional phrases**.

1. Bobby ran down the hall.

2. Patrick is hungry for his dinner.

3. The toy boat floated away from us.

Lesson 26   <u>More about Prepositional Phrases</u>

Some sentences have **more than one prepositional phrase**.

Examples: The girl <u>**with long hair**</u> ran <u>**toward the fence**</u>.

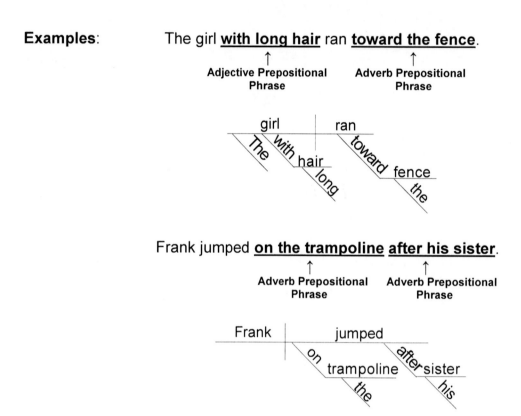

Frank jumped <u>**on the trampoline after his sister**</u>.

Some **prepositional phrases** have two **objects**. Place the **objects** on two horizontal lines, one above the other, joined by diagonal lines. This is connected to the main diagram by a diagonal line. Write the **conjunction** on the dotted line that connects the two **object** lines. Write the **preposition** on the diagonal line.

Example: The cat crawled ***through*** <u>**grass**</u> and <u>**weeds**</u>.

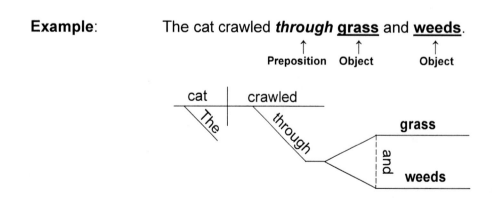

A. **Diagram** these sentences with more than one **prepositional phrase**.

   1. Through the rain my brother ran down the street.

   2. The squirrel with brown fur climbed up the tree.

B. **Diagram** these sentences with **prepositional phrases** that have two **objects**.

   1. Robert wrote a book about baseball and basketball.

   2. She slipped on snow and ice.

Lesson 27   <u>Prepositional Phrase Review</u>

A. **Diagram** these sentences with **adjective prepositional phrases**.

   1. The cat in the tree is fast.

   2. I bought a beautiful flower with red petals.

   3. We sent our aunt from Florida a postcard.

   4. My brother is the tall boy in the picture.

B. **Diagram** these sentences with **adverb prepositional phrases**.

1. The snake hid underneath the rock.

2. The gymnast is happy with her award.

3. Carlita completes her best work early during the semester.

4. The boys jumped over the fence.

C. **Diagram** these sentences with more than one **prepositional phrase**.

    1. The bracelet on her arm sparkled in the sunlight.

    2. Before the movie, I ate with my family.

D. **Diagram** this sentence with a **prepositional phrase** that has two **objects**.

    1. Your pen rolled under the books and the papers.

Chapter 5

Verbals and Verbal Phrases

Lesson 28   <u>Participles and Participial Phrases</u>

A **participle** is a **verbal** that functions as an **adjective** in a sentence, **modifying** a **noun**.

Diagram a **participle** directly **beneath** the word it **modifies**. Write the **participle** partially on a **slanted** line and partially on a **horizontal** line that extends from the slanted line.

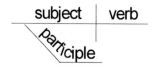

Examples: The **crying** *child* stubbed his toe.

Participle Subject

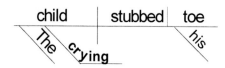

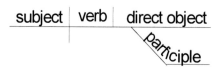

We ate the **toasted** *bread*.

Participle   Direct
Object

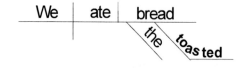

A. **Diagram** these sentences with **participles**.

1. The determined girl joined the team.

2. The trees dropped their dried leaves.

3. We saw a flying insect.

4. The married couple drove away.

When diagramming a **participial phrase**, extend the **horizontal** line to include any **objects** or **modifiers** that are part of the **participial phrase**.

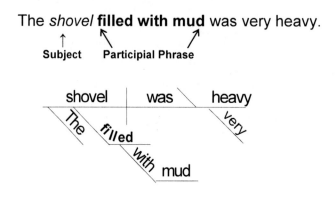

In this example, the participial phrase **filled with mud** modifies the subject **shovel**. The prepositional phrase **with mud** is diagrammed beneath the word it modifies, which in this case is the participle **filled**.

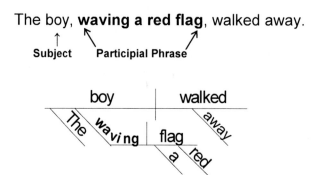

In this example, the participial phrase **waving a red flag** modifies the subject **boy**. The word **flag** is the direct object of the participle **waving**, so it is diagrammed on the horizontal line with the **participle**, separated from it by a short vertical line.

B. **Diagram** these sentences with **participial phrases**.

1. Basking in the sun the cat yawned.

2. The boy hitting the baseball is my cousin.

3. Swaying in the storm, the tree fell.

4. Wagging its tail, the dog ate quickly.

Lesson 29   <u>Gerunds and Gerund Phrases</u>

A **gerund** is a **verbal** that ends in **-ing** and functions as a **noun** in a sentence. Like a **noun**, a **gerund** can be used as a **subject**, **direct object**, **predicate noun**, or **object of a preposition**.

Diagram a **gerund** that acts as a **subject**, **direct object**, or **predicate noun** on a step that sits on a pedestal above the main line where the **noun** it replaces would be.

<u>Gerund as a Subject</u>

Example as a Subject:

Runn<u>ing</u> is good exercise.

↑
Gerund

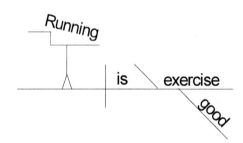

In this example, the gerund **running** is the subject of the sentence.

Gerund as a Direct Object

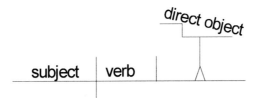

Example as a
Direct Object:

The boys like **running**.
↑
Gerund

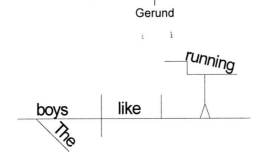

In this example, the gerund **running** is the **direct object** of the verb **like**.

~~~~~~

Gerund as a Predicate Noun

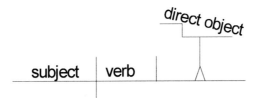

Example as a
Predicate Noun:

The best exercise is **running**.
↑
Gerund

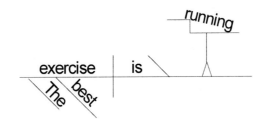

In this example, the gerund **running** is the **predicate noun** in this sentence.

Gerund as an Object of a Preposition

Diagram a **gerund** that acts as an **object of a preposition** on a line slanting down from the main horizontal line.

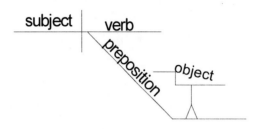

**Example as
an Object of
a Preposition:**

He was scolded for **running**.

↑
Gerund

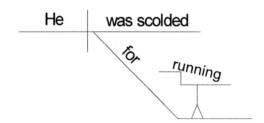

In this example, the gerund **running** is the **object** of the preposition **for** in this sentence.

A. **Diagram** these sentences with **gerunds**.

1. Painting is a great hobby.

2. My sister enjoys cleaning.

3. Mary's favorite activity is sledding.

4. Joe taught a class in skiing.

Diagram a **gerund phrase** in the same manner as a **gerund**, but extend the stepped line to include any **objects** or **modifiers** that are part of the **gerund phrase**.

Gerund Phrase as a Subject

**Example as
a Subject**:

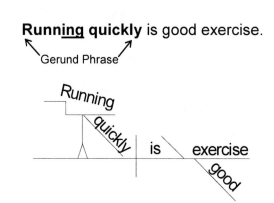

In this example, the gerund phrase **running quickly** is the **subject** of the sentence. Notice that the modifier **quickly** is diagrammed on a line slanting down from the gerund **running**.

~~~~~~

Gerund Phrase as a Direct Object

**Example as a
Direct Object**:

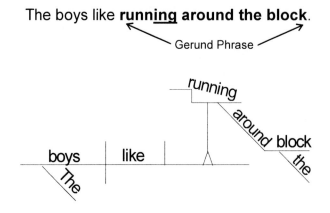

In this example, the gerund phrase **running around the block** is the **direct object** of the verb **like**. Notice that the modifying prepositional phrase **around the block** is diagrammed beneath the gerund **running**.

Gerund Phrase as a Predicate Noun

Example as a
Predicate Noun:

The best exercise is **running a marathon**.

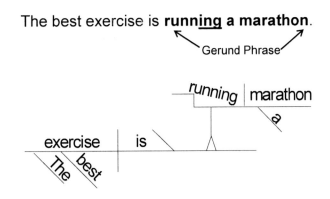

In this example, the gerund phrase **running a marathon** is the **predicate noun** in this sentence. Notice that the word **marathon** is the **direct object** of the gerund **running** and is diagrammed on the same line. The modifier **a** is diagrammed beneath the word **marathon**.

~~~~~~

Gerund Phrase as an Object of a Preposition

Example as
an Object of
Preposition:

He was scolded for **running into the pond**.

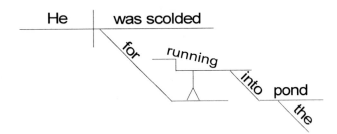

In this example, the gerund phrase **running into the pond** is the **object** of the preposition **for** in this sentence. Notice that the prepositional phrase **into the pond** modifies the gerund **running** and is diagrammed beneath it.

B. **Diagram** these sentences with **gerund phrases**.

1. Reading books on the porch is my favorite hobby.

2. I love listening to classical music.

3. His best skill was humming like a bird.

4. My mother concentrates on breathing deeply.

Lesson 30   <u>**Infinitives and Infinitive Phrases**</u>

An **infinitive** is a **verbal** consisting of the word **to** plus a **verb**. **Infinitives** are usually used a **nouns**. Like a **noun**, an **infinitive** can be used as a **subject**, **direct object**, or **predicate noun**.

Like a gerund, an **infinitive** is placed on a pedestal above the main line where the noun it replaces would be, but the line upon which the **infinitive** sits is simpler. The word **to** is placed on the slanted part of the line that attaches to the pedestal. The rest of the **infinitive** (the verb) is written on the horizontal part of the line.

<u>**Infinitive as a Subject**</u>

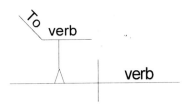

Example as
a Subject: To interrupt was rude.

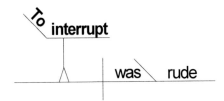

In this example, the infinitive **to interrupt** is the **subject** of the sentence.

Infinitive as a Direct Object

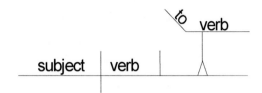

Example as a
Direct Object:

The boys want **to eat**.
↑ ↑
Infinitive

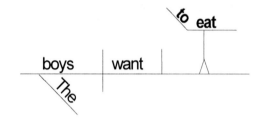

In this example, the infinitive **to eat** is the **direct object** of the sentence.

~~~~~~

Infinitive as a Predicate Noun

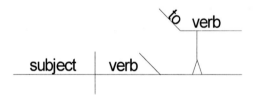

Example as a
Predicate Noun:

Our plan is **to hike**.
↑ ↑
Infinitive

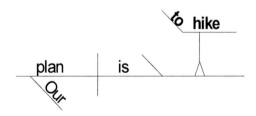

In this example, the infinitive **to hike** is the **predicate noun** of the sentence.

A. **Diagram** these sentences with **infinitives**.

1. To win is exciting.

2. My brother offered to wait.

3. My dream is to travel.

4. To race is his goal.

Diagram **infinitive phrases** in the same manner as an **infinitive**, but extend the line to include any **objects** or **modifiers** that are part of the **infinitive phrase**.

Infinitive Phrase as a Subject

Example as a Subject:

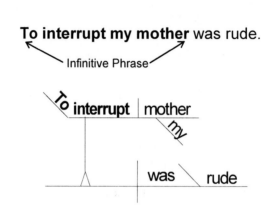

In this example, the infinitive phrase **to interrupt my mother** is the **subject** of the sentence. Notice that the word **mother** is the **direct object** of the infinitive **to interrupt** and is diagrammed on the same line. The modifier **my** is diagrammed beneath the word **mother**.

~~~~~~

Infinitive as a Direct Object

Example as a Direct Object:

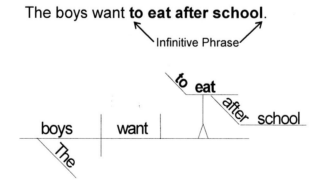

In this example, the infinitive phrase **to eat after school** is the **direct object** of the sentence. Notice that the prepositional phrase **after school** modifies the infinitive **to eat** and is diagrammed beneath it.

107

Infinitive Phrase as a Predicate Noun

**Example as a
Predicate Noun:**

Our plan is **to hike up the hill**.

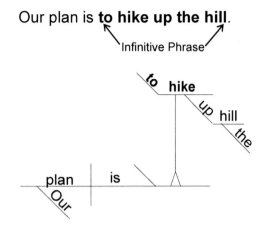

Infinitive Phrase

In this example, the infinitive phrase **to hike up the hill** is the **predicate noun** of the sentence. Notice that the prepositional phrase **up the hill** modifies the infinitive **to hike** and is diagrammed beneath it.

B. **Diagram** these sentences with **infinitive phrases**.

1. To build the roof was his job.

2. Caroline wanted to tie her shoes.

3. My goal is to run around the lake.

4. Sam decided to paint the room.

Lesson 31   <u>Verbal and Verbal Phrase Review</u>

A. **Diagram** these sentences with **participles** and **participial phrases**.

1. A startled cat dashed down the road.

2. We smelled the baking bread.

3. The ballerina, leaping into the air, entertained the audience.

4. The boy racing down the field is my cousin.

B. **Diagram** these sentences with **gerunds** and **gerund phrases**.

1. Running is my favorite exercise.

2. Brandon likes flying.

3. My hobby is sewing beautiful quilts.

4. We learned about catching large fish.

C. **Diagram** these sentences with **infinitives** and **infinitive phrases**.

1. To learn is our goal.

2. Ellen wants to paint her bedroom.

3. His job is to feed the puppy.

Chapter 6

Compound, Complex, and
Compound-Complex Sentences

Lesson 32   <u>**Compound Sentences**</u>

A sentence that consists of two or more related **independent clauses** is a **compound sentence**. The **clauses** of a **compound sentence** may be joined by both a **comma** and a **coordinating conjunction** or a **semicolon**.

Each **independent clause** of a **compound sentence** is diagrammed as a separate sentence, one above the other. Next, join both **clauses** with a dotted line. If a **conjunction** joins the clauses, place it on the dotted line.

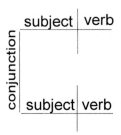

Examples: <u>Joanne read a book</u>, *but* <u>my brother wrote a poem</u>.

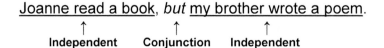

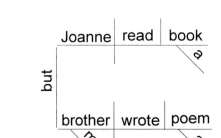

<u>We visited the museum today</u>, *and* <u>we saw a new exhibit</u>.

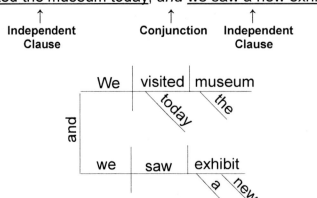

115

If a **semicolon** joins the **clauses** of a **compound sentence**, then nothing is placed on the dotted line.

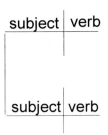

Examples:

Christopher cut his arm; he needs medication.
    ↑   ↑   ↑
   Independent Semicolon Independent
     Clause   Clause

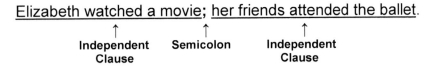

Elizabeth watched a movie; her friends attended the ballet.
    ↑   ↑   ↑
  Independent Semicolon Independent
    Clause   Clause

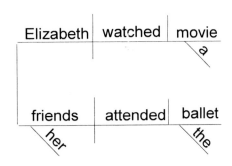

Occasionally, the **clauses** of a **compound sentence** are joined by a **semicolon** and a **conjunctive adverb** followed by a **comma**.

When a **semicolon** and a **conjunctive adverb** join the **clauses** of a **compound sentence**, then nothing is placed on the dotted line of the diagram and the **conjunctive adverb** is diagrammed in the **adverb** position on the second **clause**.

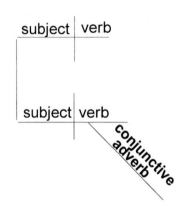

Examples: Jeremy took the wrong road; *consequently*, he missed his appointment.

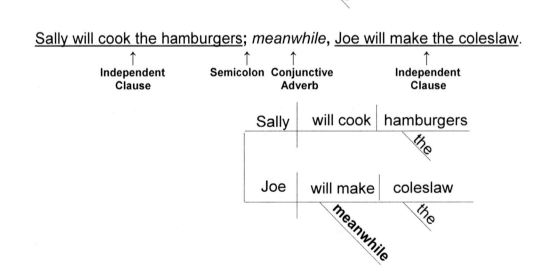

A. **Diagram** these **compound sentences**.

1. Marcus studied, and he passed the test.

2. Sally is a great person; she is my friend.

3. I wanted the red bicycle; however, I bought the black skateboard.

4. We ate dinner, and Charlie washed the dishes.

Lesson 33   <u>Complex Sentences</u>

A complex sentence contains one **independent clause** (**main clause**) and at least one **dependent clause** (**subordinate clause**). This lesson covers complex sentences that contain **adjective clauses**.

<u>Complex Sentences that Contain an Adjective Clause</u>

An **adjective clause** is a **dependent clause** used to describe a **noun**. **Relative pronouns** such as **who**, **whom**, **whose**, **which**, or **that** are used to introduce **adjective clauses**.

Diagram the **independent clause** (**main clause**) of a **complex sentence** first before diagramming the **adjective clause**.

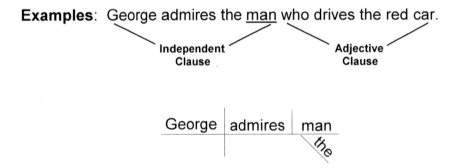

Diagram the **adjective clause** on a horizontal line below the **independent clause**. Use a dotted line to join the **relative pronoun** of the **adjective clause** to the word it modifies in the **independent clause**.

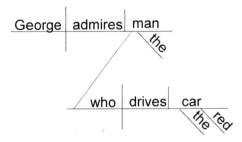

In this example, the relative pronoun **who** is the **subject** of the **adjective clause** and modifies the direct object **man** from the **independent clause**.

The <u>movie</u> **that we watched earlier** was boring.

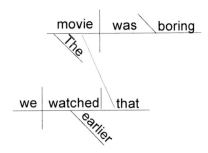

In this example, the relative pronoun **that** is the **direct object** of the **adjective clause** and modifies the subject **movie** from the **independent clause**.

~~~~~~~~~~~~~~~~~~~~~~~~~~~~~~~~~~~~

The officer caught the <u>thief</u> **whose car crashed**.

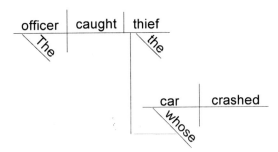

In this example, the relative pronoun **whose** is an adjective of the subject (**car**) in the **adjective clause** and modifies the direct object **thief** in the **independent clause**.

~~~~~~~~~~~~~~~~~~~~~~~~~~~~~~~~~~~~

Henry is the <u>man</u> **whom we saw yesterday**.

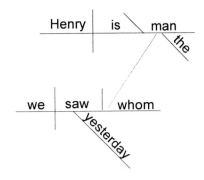

In this example, the relative pronoun **whom** is the **direct object** of the **adjective clause** and modifies the direct object **man** in the **independent clause**.

A. **Diagram** these sentences with **adjective clauses**.

1. The book that I read is interesting.

2. The woman who baked the pie is my mother.

3. I know the boy whose skateboard is red.

4. The man whom you saw is our governor.

Lesson 34   <u>Complex Sentences</u>

As we discussed in the previous lesson, a complex sentence contains one **independent clause** (**main clause**) and at least one **dependent clause** (**subordinate clause**). This lesson covers complex sentences that contain **adverb clauses**.

<u>Complex Sentences that Contain an Adverb Clause</u>

An **adverb clause** is a **dependent clause** used to describe a **verb, adjective,** or **adverb. Subordinating conjunctions** such as **after, although, as, because, before, if, since, unless, than, until, when, where,** or **while** are used to introduce **adverb clauses.** An adverb clause can occur at the beginning or the end of a sentence.

Diagram the **independent clause** (**main clause**) of a **complex sentence** first before diagramming the **adverb clause**.

Examples: Tiffany <u>saw</u> her uncle **when** she delivered the newspaper.

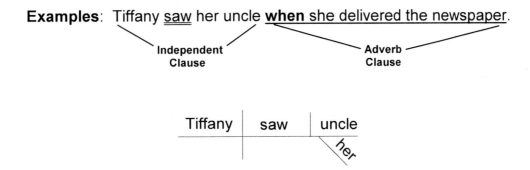

Diagram the **adverb clause** on a horizontal line below the **independent clause**. Use a dotted line to join the **verb** of the **adverb clause** to the word it modifies in the **independent clause**. Place the **subordinating conjunction** on the dotted line.

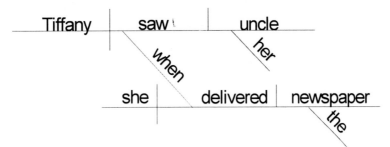

In this example, the **adverb clause** modifies the verb **saw** in the **independent clause**.

Before Ricky arrived, we ate dinner.

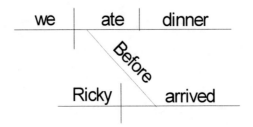

In this example, the **adverb clause** modifies the verb **ate** in the **independent clause**.

~~~~~~~~~~~~~~~~~~~~~~~~~~~~~~~~~

Bradley is taller **than** we expected.

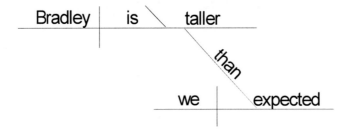

In this example, the **adverb clause** modifies the predicate adjective **taller** in the **independent clause**.

~~~~~~~~~~~~~~~~~~~~~~~~~~~~~~~~~

My sister can swim faster **than** my brother can.

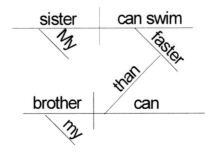

In this example, the **adverb clause** modifies the adverb **faster** in the **independent clause**.

A. Diagram these sentences with **adverb clauses.**

  1. After Ed took lessons, he could swim well.

  2. Your cat is smaller than I imagined.

  3. While I was fishing, I caught a fish.

  4. She can jump higher than Jim can.

Lesson 35   <u>Compound-Complex Sentences</u>

A **compound-complex sentence** contains **two or more independent clauses** and **one or more dependent clauses**. The diagram of a **compound-complex sentence** looks similar to that of both a **compound** and a **complex sentence**. Always diagram the **independent clauses** first. Then diagram the **dependent clause** or **clauses**.

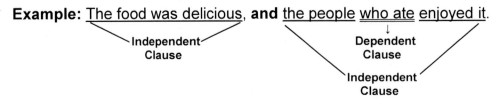

This example contains **two independent clauses** that form a compound sentence and **one dependent clause**. The **independent clauses** are **the food was delicious** and **the people enjoyed it**. The **dependent clause** is **who ate**.

Diagram the **independent clauses** first. Write the **conjunction** on the dotted line that joins the **independent clauses**.

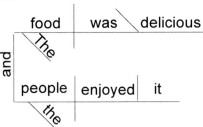

Diagram the **dependent clause** on a horizontal line below the **independent clause**. Use a dotted line to join the **dependent clause** to the word it modifies in the **independent clause**.

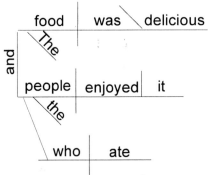

In this example, the **dependent clause** is an **adjective clause** that modifies the subject **people** from the independent clause **the people enjoyed it**.

Example: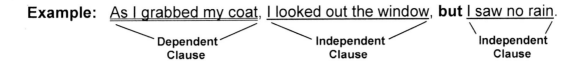

This example contains **two independent clauses** and **one dependent clause**. The independent clauses are **I looked out the window** and **I saw no rain**. The **dependent clause** is **as I grabbed my coat**.

Just as before, **diagram** the **independent clauses** first.

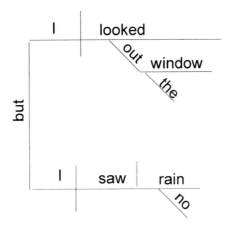

Diagram the **dependent clause** attached to the **independent clause** it **modifies**.

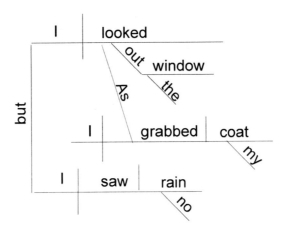

In this example, the **dependent clause** is an **adverb clause** that **modifies** the verb **looked** from the independent clause **I looked out the window**.

126

A. Diagram these **compound-complex sentences**.

1. The boy who is speaking is my cousin, and he will be staying with us.

2. While Mia reads a book, she listens to the radio and she eats popcorn.

3. I used the recipe that Marty gave me, and her cookies were delicious.

4. When the play ends, the curtain closes, and the audience applauds.

Lesson 36 <u>Compound, Complex, and Compound-Complex Sentence Review</u>

A. **Diagram** these **compound sentences**.

1. John owns a boat, but he rarely fishes.

2. The dog barked loudly, and the cat meowed softly.

3. The storm stopped; the boat arrived safely.

4. I looked for my book; however, I could not find it.

128

B. **Diagram** these sentences with **adjective clauses**.

   1. The student who passed his test was happy.

   2. The book that I read was enjoyable.

C. Diagram these sentences with **adverb clauses**.

   1. After we cleaned the house, we ate dinner.

   2. My shoes are bigger than Mom thought.

D. Diagram these **compound-complex sentences**.

   1. Joe watched a movie, but Sarah slept because she works hard.

   2. Steve wrote a poem that he submitted, and he received an award.

Chapter 7

Diagramming Other Elements

Lesson 37   <u>Appositives</u>

An **appositive** renames or helps to explain a **noun** that immediately precedes it. On a sentence **diagram**, an **appositive** is placed in **parentheses** after the word that it renames or explains.

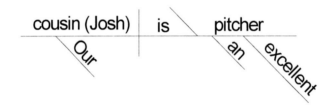

Examples: Our *cousin* **Josh** is an excellent pitcher.
                        ↑   ↑
                  Subject Appositive

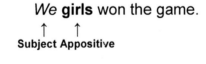

In this example, the appositive **Josh** renames the subject **cousin**.

We **girls** won the game.
  ↑   ↑
Subject Appositive

In this example, the appositive **girls** renames the subject **we**.

A. Diagram these sentences with **appositives**.

1. Our boss, Mr. Gayle, is very smart.

2. My friend Matt collects lost hubcaps.

3. The manager, Samantha, is a busy woman.

4. Our sister Shelby is extremely funny.

Lesson 38   <u>Appositive Phrases</u>

An **appositive phrase** contains an **appositive** and its **modifiers**. On a sentence **diagram**, the **appositive** is placed in **parentheses** after the word that it renames or explains. Any **modifiers** of the **appositive** are placed on slanted lines directly beneath it.

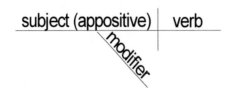

Example: *Peanut **my little puppy*** chewed my shoes.

            ↑   ↑

         Subject   **Appositive Phrase**

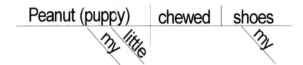

In this example, the appositive phrase **my little puppy** renames the subject **Peanut**. The **appositive** is **puppy**.

~~~~~~

subject | verb | direct object (appositive)
modifier

Example: Mom introduced *Margaret*, **a lovely woman**.

                  ↑   ↑

              Direct Object   **Appositive Phrase**

Mom | introduced | Margaret (woman)
a lovely

In this example, the appositive phrase **a lovely woman** renames the direct object **Margaret**. The **appositive** is **woman**.

A. Diagram these sentences with **appositive phrases**.

1. That woman, a talented artist, is my neighbor.

2. We welcomed Brian, the new boy.

3. Paris, a large city, is beautiful.

4. The students helped Giovanna, the girl from Italy.

Lesson 39 <u>Interjections</u>

An **interjection** is a word that **expresses strong feeling** or **emotion** and has **no grammatical relationship** to any other word in the sentence. On a sentence **diagram**, place an **interjection** on a separate line above the sentence, usually above and to the left of the **subject**.

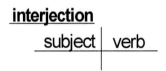

Example: **Ouch**! You hurt my foot!
↑
Interjection

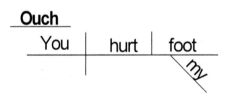

Example: **Good**, we can leave now.
↑
Interjection

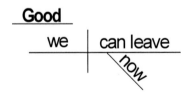

Remember to **capitalize** all words in the diagram as they are written in the sentence.

A. Diagram these sentences with **interjections**.

1. Hurray! We won the game!

2. Well, you did a great job.

3. Yikes! He scared me!

4. Wait, I am angry.

Lesson 40   <u>Nouns of Direct Address</u>

A **noun of direct address** is the **name** or **title** of a person being directly spoken to in a sentence. On a sentence **diagram**, place a **noun of direct address** on a separate line above the sentence, usually above and to the left of the **subject**.

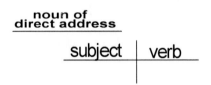

Example: **Cindy**, will you help me?

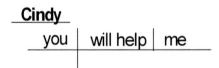

Example: Do you know the answer, **Maria**?

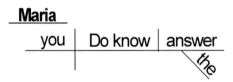

Example: Your painting, **Ricky**, was very interesting.

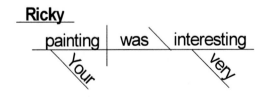

A. Diagram these sentences with **nouns of direct address**.

1. Michelle, you won the game!

2. Is that my book, Brian?

3. That new game, Jason, is very fun.

4. Your cat is cute, Marie.

Lesson 41   <u>Diagramming Other Elements Review</u>

A. Diagram these sentences with **appositives**.

1. Our teacher, Mr. Brown, is a good writer.

2. We boys washed the dishes.

B. Diagram these sentences with **appositive phrases**.

1. The insect, a small ant, ate the sugar.

2. Sonya, a professional chef, made a delicious dinner.

C. Diagram these sentences with **interjections**.

   1. Careful! That snake is venomous!

   2. Oh, Michael left early.

D. Diagram these sentences with **nouns of direct address**.

   1. Melissa, you are a good friend.

   2. I saw the new library, William.